Gomez
Liquid Skin

Hangover 8
Revolutionary Kind 14
Bring It On 21
Blue Moon Rising 30

Las Vegas Dealer 38
We Haven't Turned Arou... ..
Fill My Cup 50
Rhythm & Blues Alibi 57

California 68
Devil Will Ride 77

notation and tablature explained 84
indications sur la notation musicale et les tablatures 86
hinweise zu notation und tabulatur 88
spiegazione della notazione e dell'intavolatura 90

International
MUSIC
Publications

INTERNATIONAL MUSIC PUBLICATIONS LIMITED

ENGLAND: GRIFFIN HOUSE,
161 HAMMERSMITH ROAD, LONDON W6 8BS
GERMANY: MARSTALLSTR. 8. D-80539 MUNCHEN
DENMARK: DANMUSIK, VOGNMAGERGADE 7
DK 1120 KOBENHAVNK

WARNER/CHAPPELL MUSIC

CANADA: 40 SHEPPARD AVE. WEST, SUITE 800
TORONTO, ONTARIO M2N 6K9
SCANDINAVIA: P.O. BOX 533, VENDEVAGEN 85 B
S-182 15, DANDERYD, SWEDEN
AUSTRALIA: P.O. BOX 353
3 TALAVERA ROAD, NORTH RYDE N.S.W. 2113

Nuova CARISH S.p.A.

ITALY: VIA CAMPANIA, 12
20098 S. GIULIANO MILANESE (MI)
ZONA INDUSTRIALE SESTO ULTERIANO
FRANCE: 20, RUE DE LA VILLE-L'EVEQUE,
75008 PARIS
www.carisch.com

WARNER BROS. PUBLICATIONS
THE GLOBAL LEADER IN PRINT

USA: 15800 NW 48TH AVENUE
MIAMI, FL 33014

Music Transcribed by Artemis Music Limited, Pinewood Road, Iver Heath, Bucks SL0 0NH
Printed by The Panda Group · Haverhill · Suffolk CB9 8PR · UK · Binding by Haverhill Print Finishers

Photo Pages: Most photos by Jerry Hawkins, some by Steve Fellows, some by Dajon Everett

14·99

This interview took place on Tuesday 21st December 1999 at around 4.00pm. Those present were Ian Ball, Paul Blackburn, Tom Gray, Ben Ottewell, Olly Peacock, Dajon Everett and Steve Fellows.

Ben: What kind of mullet have you just drawn on yourself?

Olly: I've given myself various different mullets

Steve: Do you want me to find out what the last one was?

Tom: Is that CD all signed?

Dajon: Yeah

Steve: Ok…that'll…let's talk about 'Liquid Skin' a bit….erm

Ian: Lesbian

Steve: For the music book

Ian: For the music book

Steve: Erm….let's talk about Hangover…..again (mass laughter and groans) Oh crikey!

Olly: What about this one, Ben?

Steve: I can write about that…I can answer that…I know the answers.

Ian: What do you remember of that song, Blacks?

Tom: It got written in Ilkley

Olly: Yeah, we were all sat around weren't we? It was one of the…first….I dunno. It was fairly early on in Ilkley…and one night Ian had got his mikes out

Ian: Got the mikes out geezer

Olly: Got the four track out

Ian: Put it in the room

Olly: And, er, we jammed it

Ian: Then we looped it and played over the top of it

Olly: Yeah, it was a mistake when you went (raspberry sound) on the keyboard, then we went…oh, it had all kind of modulated down a little

Ian: Yeah

Olly: Is that bit in the song?

Ian: That's it…there's some Chinese strings in there. Strings played by Chinese people

Tom: Yeah, there're lots of people playing Chinese strings. I remember the original sitar line in the room we played on something that Ben…played by me, but on something weird that Ben had made with a 12 string guitar

Steve: By the way, that's in the office if you're wondering where it is

Tom: Something that he'd…in fact it nearly destroyed some guitar but it made a really good noise

Ben: It was progressive

Tom: Ben had basically made like er…a…Ben..Benetar. It's called a Benetar. He made Pat Benetar and I was playing it in our kitchen…no, in the lounge

Ian: Pat Benetar it is

Steve: Pat Benetar. Ok, Revolutionary Kind (silence, then muttering). I love that it's one of my favourite tunes of all time

Olly: Me and you…in Haremere

Ben: In various stages

Olly: And it kind of re-appeared

Tom: Vocal in a balcony in Leeds

Olly: Re-appeared in Haremere after…

Dajon: Haremere was the…

Olly: A long time…any kind of

Ben: Started as…

Tom: Written on a, on a summers day on a balcony in Leeds facing the house in which the guy who wrote 'Swallows and Amazons' grew up in…'s where I used to live. Wrote it, went over to Sheffield,

wrote a mad chorus with Ben in which we shouted 'dancing' over and over again and modulated. Then we played it for a while and it used to segue…in live shows. In our first gigs it used to segue into 'Get Myself Arrested' didn't it?

Olly: Yeah

Tom: Then we got bored shitless with it and stopped playing it altogether

Ben: Tried to record it and it fucked up most royally

Tom: So…yeah…royally. It went all soft, when it was a rockin' tune

Olly: And in the chorus kind of…dancing

Tom: It went all, soft. It just went all sort of 'middle of the roadey' and it was supposed to be rocking

Olly: And then that's when we came back to it again and sort of really kicked ass again in Haremere where we stumbled along choosing…

Ben: Tom had done a version of it. Tom had written a new kind of chorus for it.

Ian: Oh yeah, the catastrophic 'ba-ba-ba-ba-ba' (all laugh)

Tom: It didn't really work in the end…but the chorus stuck the strange backing vocals left the building there…

Ben: Which was a shame! (more laughter)

Tom: Man, you got to try stuff!

Steve: Oh yeah, absolutely

Tom: Ba-ba-ba-ba-ba (more laughter)

Ben: It was a 'little drummer boy' moment that didn't quite work

Tom: It was a similar idea to what actually eventually happened…but less 'Bing'. Nice little drums going 'ba-ba-ba-ba-ba' sound better than someone going 'ba-ba-ba-ba-ba' over and over and over again

Olly: We had that monstrous stereo mike in there didn't we? When we went into stereo world

Ian: Stereo…yeah, that was a good mike

Olly: We did all our kind of…

Steve: That soundfield thing..

Olly: …Background effects. You were doing basically a heron really weren't you, in the background

Ian: I was going…(ensemble bird impressions)

Olly: I was breathing like…

Ben: We were whistling…

Ian: Oh yeah, you were doing that sexy Marvin Gaye… (breathy sigh)

Ben: I was whistling

Olly: You were whistling

Ben: (Whistles) (more bird calls and whistles)

Olly: Aaaah

Ben: It sounds like…I dunno…It was good though

Ian: I really like the fade out on that song

Olly: Yeah, it is a good fade out

Ben: I sang about 18 different tracks, didn't I? …On top of each other

Olly: Still a big fan of that

Ben: What, the Moog? Oh yeah, the Moog track, yeah

Olly: I remember doing it a couple of times…then we just got it

Ian: Sounds really good…good tune

Steve: It's great…that's a small novel about…

Olly: Yeah. Still can't do it live

Steve: I live for the day…

Olly: We will get it sorted

Ben: We'll just play along to an A-DAT

Tom: Put the whole thing on an A-DAT…and have an…all walk

Olly: All of us just get machines

Tom: Everyone get to the front of the stage

and have a laugh making noises along to the A-DAT

Olly: Yeah

Tom: I don't know why we should bother…

Steve: I always felt like…why beat yourselves up trying to…

Olly: I always thought about doing that originally…

Steve: Make it more a part of the show kind of thing

Olly: We should all have machines at the front of the stage and all just go (makes drum sounds)

Ben: Strip all the vocals off it

Tom: Yeah, synthesisers, noises, basically just turn into Add N to X for no apparent reason…halfway through the show…

Steve: Ok…Bring It On

Tom: Oh, Christ, that's really,,,

Steve: It's really long ago isn't it, that?

Ben: Yeah, that's an old tune!

Steve: 'Cos I remember you playing it just before we were about to set off on the Embrace tour

Ben: We mixed it at Max's one day

Steve: Bring It On?

Ben: Yeah

Steve: Is there a version of that?

Ben: Yeah

Ian: Four-track version…yeah…we did it on a four track but erm…

Ben: The middle bit sounds fucking ace, doesn't it!

Ian: The problem was…we could never do the vocals on…

Ben: Yeah

Ian: On four track, so it's basically an instrumental version on the four track

Tom: We didn't have enough room, did we, for all the vocals. We were wanting to do the vocals

Ben: But we mixed on…we actually mixed that at Max's with, a version of it, with all the other stuff that we mixed there

Ian: From the first…first album. I don't think it's as good as the new version though

Steve: I'd completely forgotten about that

Ben: But there is a version of it, isn't there?…Somewhere

Ian: Could be

Ben: But that's how old it is…very old

Steve: That'd be..yoosh…early…

Tom: But I mean I was in my second year at University so I wrote the 'if I was' bit in Leon's room…I'd sing in Leon's room

Olly: How long ago was that?

Tom: First year I was in…Oh, shit…it is quite a long time ago actually

Ben: About three years ago

Tom: It's when I was in the second year at University. So, it's when you were in the third year. So, when were you in the third year?

Olly: Is it three and a half…three and a half years ago

Tom: Three years ago

Olly: It's over three years

Tom: That's when it was written that…

Olly: And then…did we do another version? We did another version didn't we? Did we go back and do another version then, when we were doing Bring It On?

Ben: I think we were starting one or something. I don't know…

Olly: And that sounded terrible

Ben: I think we left it…

Tom: It was the electric guitar that Ian did…sorted it all out…(sings riff)

Ian: Oh yeah, trying to make it sound like

Pete Townsend

Tom: That was nice

Ben: Without the big fuckin'…did you ever see Pete Townsend when he's doing his….brilliant…

Steve: Once, apparently, he was playing a Strat and he did that, windmilled, and the tremolo arm went right through his hand…

Dajon: I saw the gig after that actually, well, on telly…he had it all bandaged up

Olly: Yeah, I heard

Ian: Ouch!

Steve: Apparently, he took the guitar off and held it up in front of the people with the tremolo arm sticking out of his hand and supported…you know…like that

Olly: They had some good punch ups that band

Steve: Anyway..er…Blue Moon Rising

Ben: Did we finish Bring It On then?

Steve: I think so…it just sort of went off into The Who

Dajon: That's alright

Tom: Blue Moon Rising was done…er…at a single…er, we were recording B-sides for a single weren't we

Olly: That was in May

Steve: Black Wing

Tom: At Black Wing. Which singles were we recording B-sides for?…It was for Get Myself Arrested

Steve: Yeah

Tom: It was Old School Shirt…Pick Up The Pieces…

Steve: Cowboy Song

Olly: You did it by accident, didn't you…you just did that version and it sounded really good

Tom: Yeah

Olly: I was in Sri Lanka at the time

Ian: Or was it Piccadilly we were doing B-sides for? Oh, we did Pussyfooting didn't we?

Tom: It was Pussyfooting and Old School Shirt

Ian: That's on Piccadilly, isn't it?

Tom: Oh no it's not, it's Piccadilly, it's the one with Pick Up The Pieces. Pick Up The Pieces is an ace tune

Ian: It's Dajon on the drums, isn't it? 'Cos you were…

Dajon: Yeah, Olly was in Sri Lanka

Olly: And then I did…

Ian: The second verse…

Olly: The second verse

Tom: Gomez fans like that a lot, Pick Up The Pieces

Olly: Yeah, they do

Tom: So I'm told

Ben: Gomez fans?

Olly: Yeah!

Ben: It's a Gomez tune isn't it?…It figures!

Steve: It's all very logical

Tom: It's a shame it turns into psychedelic Cagney and Lacey at the end

Ben: Yeah…Well, no, it's not a shame at all

Tom: I'm only joking; it's not a shame at all. It's very nice, but it does

Steve: Can we get back to Blue Moon Rising?

Ben: I was sat on a stool…

Ian: Creaking

Ben: Creaking away through the entire track

Steve: Blue Moon?

Ben: Yeah

Olly: And that inspired the entire track

Ben: I was sat on a stool

Tom: I think I've got the A-shoes…that's that

Dajon: Was that when we discovered text messaging on mobile phones as well?

We spent like five hours or something…

Tom: Yeah, we'd all brought mobile phones when we did Blue Moon Rising, 'cos me and Blacks played a game on our Snakey on the Nokia for hours. In fact I lost my mobile phone…that very session…

Olly: Allegedly, it just got misplaced

Tom: Oh yeah, 'allegedly', can't say libellous things

Steve: Somebody nicked it, didn't they?

Ben: I think there were more flukes in that song than anything

Tom: Everybody wrote a line for that song…that's what…that guitar

Ben: Yeah, everyone…all the guitar lines were just like, sit down, do a guitar line

Tom: Yeah

Dajon: And they all just worked

Ben: And they all just worked. It's all flukes, compiled with bits and pieces of, like, flukes

Tom: It's just a really basic blues tune…full of nice flukes (laughs)

Ben: Big…big…flukey thing

Tom: Good old, little old blues tune

Steve: Anymore? Nope…Las Vegas Dealer

Tom: That's been around for ages as well, hasn't it?

Ben: Away with the faeries

Tom: Away with the faeries…but the Ian had had that for ages anyway, hadn't you?

Ian: Hmm

Tom: You'd had it for bloody…

Ian: That was the…I wrote that line and then about two hours later the author Laurie Lee died…which really freaked me out

Olly: Oh yeah, yeah

Ian: And the words 'Laurie Lee' have absolutely no meaning to me whatsoever…they just sort of…

Ben: They came to you

Steve: The 'Cider with Rosie' guy

Ian: Yeah, well I found out he died about 2 hours after I'd written those lines

Tom: 'As I walked out one summer's morning'

Ian: A bit spooky…and then this dealer that we met up with in Las Vegas was called Laura Lee as well

Ben: No he wasn't

Ian: The chip dispenser

Ben: The woman was…

Ian: Yeah

Steve: The croupier

Ian: Yeah, that's it. The chip dispenser

Ben: The croupier was called Laura Lee and the dealer on the table was…

Ian: Gary Beck, no…

Ben: Gary whatever his name is out of Extreme's dad and also an actor who acted in that Scorcese picture about…Casino and he promised to take us to some Blues bars and we drunk so much White Russian that he actually morphed into Nuno Bettancourt's dad…then, so the tune's about a Las Vegas dealer

Ian: Yeah, a dead author

Ben: A Las Vegas Dealer

Ian: And a dodgy eighties band

Ben: And betting as well

Steve: Hence the pun on betting and Bettancourt

Ian: Always double your money when a good tune comes on in the casino

Ben: Yeah, when a good tune comes on

Olly: I remember being very drunk when we recorded that…really late upstairs in Parr Street, really smashed

Ian: Yeah, we did that in the tiny studio didn't we

Olly: We were hammered

Ian: Made it up as we went along. The entire section

Olly: Yeah, you on the piano doing the 'doodle-a-da'

Ben: Oh that bit! Yeah, yeah

Olly: Time signatures that were never really properly laid

Steve: I remember you nearly exploding trying to get that bit in the middle

Ben: I remember you guys…I wasn't there and I'd done the bass line for the other bit…

Olly: It was like 'give me two minutes and I'll get it' and stuff

Ben: And you guys had taken, like, I don't know, you'd been intense in this conversation. I'd gone out to get something, you'd finished this…this bit, da da da da-da da da-da, and I had to go and do the bass line, and you'd been doing it for an hour or something…I came back and you were 'just fucking do it, it goes like this da-da da-da-da-da da, it's dead easy' and I was like, 'what the fuck is this?'

Olly: We'd struggled for ages, all of us

Tom: We were all playing it weren't we? 'Cos I mean E was on the piano, I was on the organ, you were playing the drums, simultaneously

Olly: And we were all trying to figure it out

Ben: And you'd all like kind of done this thing and then I came in completely fresh, 'cos I'd gone to get a sausage roll or something like that

Olly: Pasty

Ben: And I came back and you were like, 'just do the bass, just do it'

Tom: Come on man, sort it out!

Olly: I enjoyed doing those claps with Ken. I remember cutting those

Ian: The claps were the very last thing that went on it, weren't they?

Olly: Yeah, they were down

Ian: Just as we mixed a version of it Ken and OI started clapping, just after we'd finished the mix…and then it was like…well…

Ben: Got to get that

Ian: Those two legged it back in there and just recorded it straight on top of the vocal track and then remixed by putting the clapping in, which is a favourite in Barcelona…that song…of all places

Ben: Surprisingly enough

Ian: In Barcelona, both heavily into the Spanish vibe

Ben: It's turned into a big Spanish kind of…opening section

Tom: Bit of romantic Mediterranean bravado

Ben: Which they're very keen on over there

Ian: Aye

Steve: What's after Dealer? Is it We Haven't Turned Around?

Olly: Could be

Ian: Haven't got a fucking clue…last thing I remember about that song was watching the…er, string players come in at Abbey Road and legging down the stairs with a spliff and a bottle of wine shouting…

Ben: Shouting

Ian: Shouting instructions out at these…

Ben: 'He's right, is he right? He's right isn't he? That guy's right, there, that feller there, you're right'

Ian: The viola guy and the cello guy were discussing which note to play and I heard that one of them was right and everyone else was saying, 'no, no it can't be that note'

Ben: Funny thing I remember about that was this guy. We had a big bag of skunk in there and this, er, like the guy who was kind of…

Tom: One of the members of the orchestra, shall we say

Ben: Yeah, one of the other members of the orchestra. While this guy was listening to it and going 'this, this, this' he kind of snuck up to me and said 'can you just sneak a bit of this in my roll up?'

Ian: That was good

Ben: He kind of snuck up. That was very funny

Ian: Some good basket playing on that song. like the baskets

Ben: Good shaking of baskets by Dajon

Steve: Baskets?

Olly: Baskets

Dajon: Kashishi's is the, er, technical term

Ian: Baskets is a better name though, isn't it?

Steve: So, it would be Fill My Cup

Tom: Fill My Cup, don't know about that one. We played it at, er…

Olly: I remember coming round to your house and I think you were playing it and I remember playing it in…

All: Yellow Arch

Tom: …rehearsal studio, with a big electric guitar and him picking up the bass and making a big, fuzzy noise. That was all there was to that song

Olly: And everybody made a big noise…

Dajon: And there was another piece of that song that was quite bizarre…do you remember we were staying in a hotel in Sheffield…The Holiday Inn…You guys were going through it, and some bloke walked into the hotel room, said 'alright', sat down, who I presumed you two knew

Ian: Yeah, he was from a band

Dajon: The 60ft Dolls?

Ian: Yeah

Dajon: The drummer out of the 60ft Dolls, that's who he was. He just sat there for five minutes silently

Ian: 'Cos me and Tom were writing the bridges…'cos you said 'write me something in E'

Tom: Yeah, we were doing the bridges

Ian: He came in

Tom: He came in. He sat behind us

Dajon: Yeah

Tom: We didn't even notice him. Well, I didn't sort of…

Ian: We only found out who he was later on, didn't we?

Tom: Yeah, yeah. He sat there for a while, watched us, then silently walked out of the room again. It was very strange

Ben: He was fucked though, wasn't he?

Tom: They were all fucked…it was some weird trespass

Ben: Was it that night when, like…

Tom: Oh, no

Ben: It wasn't that night, was it?

Tom: It was in the Holiday Inn

Ben: Yeah, that was where the…

Tom: It wasn't a mad night, it wasn't on your knees with the married couple night

Olly: On your knees with the married couple?

Tom: Oh, we don't need to discuss that

Steve: I won't ask!

Ian: There's also, er, natural…natural disasters on that song…there's a tornado, avalanches, a volcano and, er…fire, like a forest fire

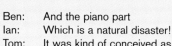

Ben: And the piano part

Ian: Which is a natural disaster!

Tom: It was kind of conceived as a kind of like, er…surf meets the Pixies type of thing

Ben: But then it turned into a kind of at sea, sea-sick tune

Tom: But then it turned into skate-punk in the middle

Ian: Oh yeah, we put the drum kit in a tank and drove it through a rock pool

Tom: That song was just a laugh to record because we'd…everything had just got effects on it

Ben: Yeah

Tom: Just about

Ben: I like the effect on my guitar which came out of the zoom thing

Ian: Yeah

Ben: Whurgh-weeurgh

Ian: Capture the…who wouldn't like that sound?

Tom: J. J. Cale

Ian: J. J. Cale probably wouldn't like that sound

Steve: Julian Bream…good sound

Tom: Oh, you like it then?

Ian: Kenny Everett would have liked that song, I reckon

Ben: Yeah, Kenny Everett would have taken that and made it his own I think

Olly: That song was for Kenny

Tom: Kenny's dead now guys, just forget about it

Ian: Oh well

Steve: With heavy hearts we must move on to Rhythm & Blues Alibi, controversial song in its early stages…

Ian: It was rubbish for a long time that song

Ben: That was the song that was written over the telephone

Tom: It's a purler that song

Ben: It was written over the phone

Olly: What's that song by Whitney Houston?

Steve: It's not right but it's OK

Olly: Was it that one?….I remember being inspired by that

Ian: Oh yeah, yeah, the drum machine track was….

Tom: Stylistically…

Ben: We did a version that not everyone liked, so we did another one

Steve: Ian absolutely loathed it

Tom: I think we did about seven

Olly: The last one went on the album

Steve: After Rhythm and Blues, now is it Rosalita?

Tom: Yeah, wrote that in Ilkley. Had that done, played it together, wrote all the lyrics one night that was it. Recorded it. Ba-da-boom

Ben: Yeah, recorded it then took some stuff away from it…discovered…re-discovered it, forgot about it

Tom: It was lost

Ben: Ken's responsible for that coming back actually, 'cos he just said 'that's an ace tune'. We listened to it and said 'Ken, you're right'

Olly: Yeah. I think it was when we were mixing down a lot of songs quickly…certain songs that could be done in a couple of hours. By the end Ken was going on and on about it…and we all then agreed…'cos that was a bit controversial, wasn't it? It's got Ian on bongos as well

Ben: Ken takes full credit for that

Olly: Yeah

Tom: Love song, what do you say?…Sweet

little song about someone leaving someone else, that's it really. Lots of songs been written about that and lots more will be too…tra-la-la

Steve: Ok…big one…part one…California

Olly: What did we do first on that song?…We went through four stages. I remember having a really odd way of trying to record it

Ian: Yeah, we had the middle and the end from another song

Olly: Yeah

Ian: And me and Ben pieced it together in the cupboard in Seattle

Ben: Seattle, yeah

Ian: Last night of the American tour…just before the onslaught of the Tequila water-pistols

Tom: That tune starts a long time ago

Olly: I remember it being bogged down…wasn't gonna work

Ben: Wasn't it the first thing we recorded for Liquid Skin? The summer song…'cos you showed up in the studio and you'd just got a Doctor Groove

Tom: Yeah, it was the first sample I made on Doctor Groove

Ben: Yeah, and we recorded the sample and just pissed around with it while we were waiting for other people to arrive

Tom: Yeah, that was it. That was what it was. We did it when we were waiting for everyone else to get there. It was just a groove thing…that…eeyayah…backwards thing…Basically we stripped out the old song which was a totally different thing and er…

Ben: Kept the instrumental

Tom: Kept the instrumental…bit. The groove…kept the groove and applied it

Ben: There were loads of little bits of songs floating around so we stuck them all together

Tom: It's really weird…that song's got more accidents in it than Blue Moon Rising even…'cos, like, there was that other song. Well, those two samples don't go together, which is really strange

Ben: No, they don't go together

Tom: They nearly do (laughs)

Ian: Nearly's good enough innit?

Ben: The groove's a bit different you know…so it's…then there's, yeah, there's just a big rock moment in the middle

Tom: Space rock

Ben: Space rock

Tom: When you, Steve, kick off with your fantastic guitar

Ben: There's a rather prominent snare beat

Olly: Yeah, we were going on and on for ages…get that snare up…get that snare up. They were going; 'Is that enough?' You were going; 'No, turn it up, turn it up'

Ian: A trio of pigeons…

Olly: A lot of ideas coming in and out all the time

Ben: Loads of guitars all over the place

Tom: Not really sure. I mean not really…not thought through, not considered…just…barely arranged

Olly: It felt as though it could have collapsed easy

Tom: Yeah, I think that was it. We were just hanging on a kind of…

Ben: We were amazed that it worked by the end of it

Tom: 'Cos we were just dropping in…like guessing stuff as well. Like dropping in that stuff from the Summer Song, going; 'How long do you reckon? Eight bars?' Yeah…go on then, you know it just…and not really knowing what it was going to sound like by the end, because we weren't dropping it into the middle. We were just adding bits on and adding bits on…so there was no way of knowing, by the end of the song, whether it was going to work

Ben: We had a basic arrangement for it but it only went as far as…that bit…that bit…that bit

Steve: I do remember the moment when E said; 'It's gonna work, it's gonna work'

Ian: Finally got the bass on it…realised it did actually…

Ben: And your guitar tied it all together as well…'cos it was…that was running through it…bit of cosmic blue

Tom: As soon as the song had a climax I think really…'cos it made sense…'cos that was the problem really. I mean, although it hasn't got a kind of composition to it. It…it reaches a point and then kind of relaxes from it, which is good. It's kind of got a movement in it which, despite the fact that, I think if it hadn't been there, would have fallen a bit flat but it hits a mark…When all those guitars come flying in…it kind of rises to the occasion. That's why it works

Olly: It's a really good structure

Tom: Like the big ending…It's like watching a nice long film

Steve: A rollercoaster of a track

All: Yeah

Ben: Like classical music

Olly: Definitely

Steve: Ok, er…

Tom: But not quite as clever

Ben: Cleverer than Bach…But not as clever as Stravinsky

Tom: No idea…He was very clever

Ben: Very, very, very clever

Olly: Very clever

Ben: Bach!

Tom: When was Stravinsky alive?

Steve: Was it…early part of this century, 1900's?

Tom: You know he…there's another thing I found out. This is quite an interesting fact. You know Fantasia by Walt Disney? Stravinsky liked the bit they'd done to his tune so much that he asked if he could write another bit so they so they could have …they could do another bit in Fantasia…yeah, just a little

Ben: Did Walt say 'no'?

Tom: No, they didn't have room to do it.

Steve: Fancy turning down Stravinsky

Tom: Walt Disney said, 'Stravinsky, no!'

Ian: You can't fit into the budget

Ben: Fantasia

Tom: Well, no it's, Fantasia 2000….it's only got one of the original scenes but the rest of the film's been completely replaced

Ben: But they've got an orchestra though…playing along to the fucking thing, they're gonna have an orchestra

Tom: A feature film made for I-Max

Ben: Yeah, it's gonna be incredible

Ian: Sounds good to me

Tom: 'Cos the original conception of Fantasia, I was telling Steve this earlier, was that it was originally made…It was Walt

Disney's ridiculous middle-brow idea that he was going to sell classical music to the masses and the idea was that each scene was going to be replaced over the years and it was never going to be, like, one solid film. It was gonna be extra animations added to the classical music but it was a flop. When they brought it out it was a massive flop so...it never got updated. But they sold it on video, like over the last ten years...just made millions and millions and billions of dollars...but it made so much money that they spent all the money on making this massive...It's only got 'The Sorcerer's Apprentice', the bit with Mickey in it, from the original film...the rest of it's completely different

Ben: It hasn't got the elephant thing?

Tom: It's got all new scenes, massively...yeah, but they've spent...it's gonna be incredible

Ben: Oh yeah, I saw some of the animation at I-Max a couple of months ago...fucking good. These guys with paint and stuff climbing up ladders and just chucking it...really simple stuff

Tom: Walt's grandson whose made it

Ben: Really?

Tom: So it's like a love thing...so it's like a...you know what I mean. There'll be things to outdo the hippopotami and the tulips. No doubt using modern computer techniques...3D...and on an I-Max screen...wow!

Ben: It's gonna be great

Tom: That's going to be fucking incredible!

Steve: Anyway...

Tom: Take some serious acid and go and watch Fantasia 2000 at the I-Max

Ian: Ouch!

Tom: That's what...Can we go back to the Southport Interview and write that as what we're going to be doing for next year. Taking some serious acid and going to an I-Max to watch Fantasia 2000

Steve: You want that in the Southport Interview?

Tom: No, not at all...ridiculous

Steve: That's the thing you don't want to do...nothing that's going to get you in the shit at home

Tom: All right, yeah. Ok

Steve: All right, Devil Will Ride

Ben: A controversial tune again

Ian: Last track

Steve: Oh, in it's final form it wasn't controversial was it?

Ben: It was touch and go whether it was going to...

Steve: For a while...but at the end it was...

Tom: It was just dead lucky that you bought a vocoder, Steve. If you hadn't bought a vocoder I don't think that song would exist. In fact it wouldn't...You brought a vocoder with you to Haremere Hall which you'd just bought and you bought me a whammy as well...Which was great

Steve: And you had 'em both didn't you?

Tom: I had 'em both off you, yeah...and er...I was playing the vocoder and just basically started singing through the vocoder over some chords that I'd had forever and came up with that...'if you will'...

Ben: Sounded boss

Tom: That...that melody thing...and Ian added the whole 'bye bye baby'

Ian: The other song

Tom: The other song...for ages, and we just

stuck 'em together and there you have it...and then...

Ian: The end section was the hardest bit 'cos it went mental then...

Olly: It went too monstrous...we had to contain it basically

Ian: A bassoon too far, wasn't it?

Ben: We put too many instruments on it

Dajon: So much going on that nothing was very defined

Tom: We actually made some really, really, really; really big white noise recording everything it was possible to record. But, then you discover that good white noise is really hard to do...if anyone tries it...just a little pointer there...anyone trying to make really big white noise

Olly: I think one of the great things about that was just being able to record it a Abbey Road...I remember being in there...having a few shivers down the...old...er, spine

Ian: Yeah, it was cool

Tom: We had the trumpets and everything and it was just cutting it down, getting the trumpets back on...

Ian: It got remixed an hour before the album was supposed to be in

Steve: Well, it was never...quite...

Ian: Yeah...but it was the last song in the studio

Steve: Can we have this album please?

Ben: Where's our album?...We've paid for it...where is it?

Steve: Have you finished yet?

Ben: Then the Mojaves came down and sung...Robbie Robertson was there, but we failed to get him involved

Tom: Did you not get Robbie Robertson?

Ben/Olly: No (sadly)

Steve: Robbie Robertson?

Ben: Yeah

Olly: He was in the studios in er...

Ian: Strongroom

Steve: Really?

Ben: Yeah

Tom: So you should have had him down

Olly: Well, we were going to

Ben: Well, he was leaving wasn't he? And Simon was like; 'that's Robbie Robertson', he just kind of...walked out...(silence for a few moments)

Ian: Good trumpets though

Ben: Yeah, very good trumpets

Ian: Very, very good brass part...saved the end of the song...and made the song

Olly: That's also where we got the er...sounds for the very start of the album

Tom: Bu-bum

Ian: It's us waiting

Olly: We put the tape on...with everybody talking and things...unbeknownst to everybody...just to see if we could get some...then we went back and found the best part and stuck it on the very start of Hangover

Ben: Which was nice

Ian: Very silly

Tom: Right, that's it...It's time to go and do some work

Hangover

**Words and Music by
Thomas William Gray, Oliver James Peacock,
Ian Thomas Ball, Paul Blackburn,
Benjamin Joseph Ottewell and Matt Turner**

Chorus (E)

Be my head of a girl,— be my head of a girl.

Gtr. 2 (acous.)

Gtr. 1: tacet   Gtr. 3 (elec.): w/Fill 1 (x3)

Be my head of a girl,— be my head of a girl.

Gtr. 3: tacet

Gtr. 1

Gtr. 2: w/Rhy. Fig. 2 (x24)

Fill 1

Gtr. 3 (elec.)

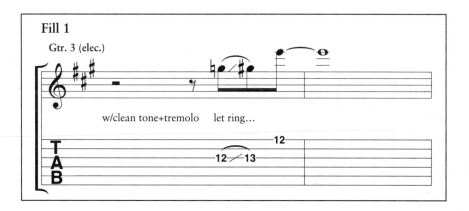

w/clean tone+tremolo   let ring...

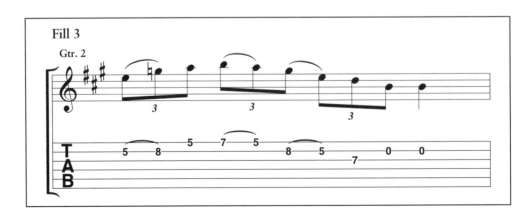

Revolutionary Kind

Words and Music by
Thomas William Gray, Oliver James Peacock,
Ian Thomas Ball, Paul Blackburn
and Benjamin Joseph Ottewell

Verse (E)

(1.) Keep_____ on kick - ing shit,____ keep
(2.) Keep on in the jun - gle with____ your

Gtr. 2

Gtr. 1: w/Fig. 1 *(x4)*
2° Gtr. 3: w/Fill 1 *(x2)*

run - ning off the rails.____
tech - no - ca - li - ties.____

Keep____ on pick -
Keep____ on lap -

_ ing the dirt____ from 'neath your____ fin - ger - nails.____
_ ping up____ your chemi - cal____ du - ty free.____

Fill 1

Gtr. 3 (elec.)

P.M.
w/clean tone, delay+phaser

16

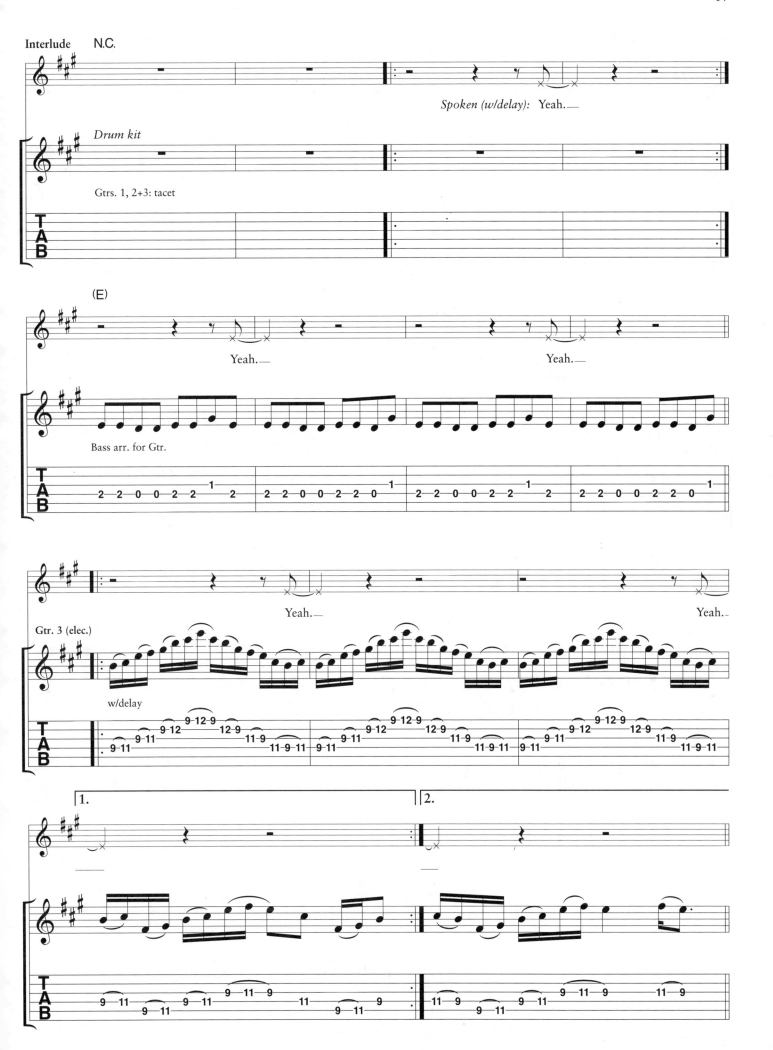

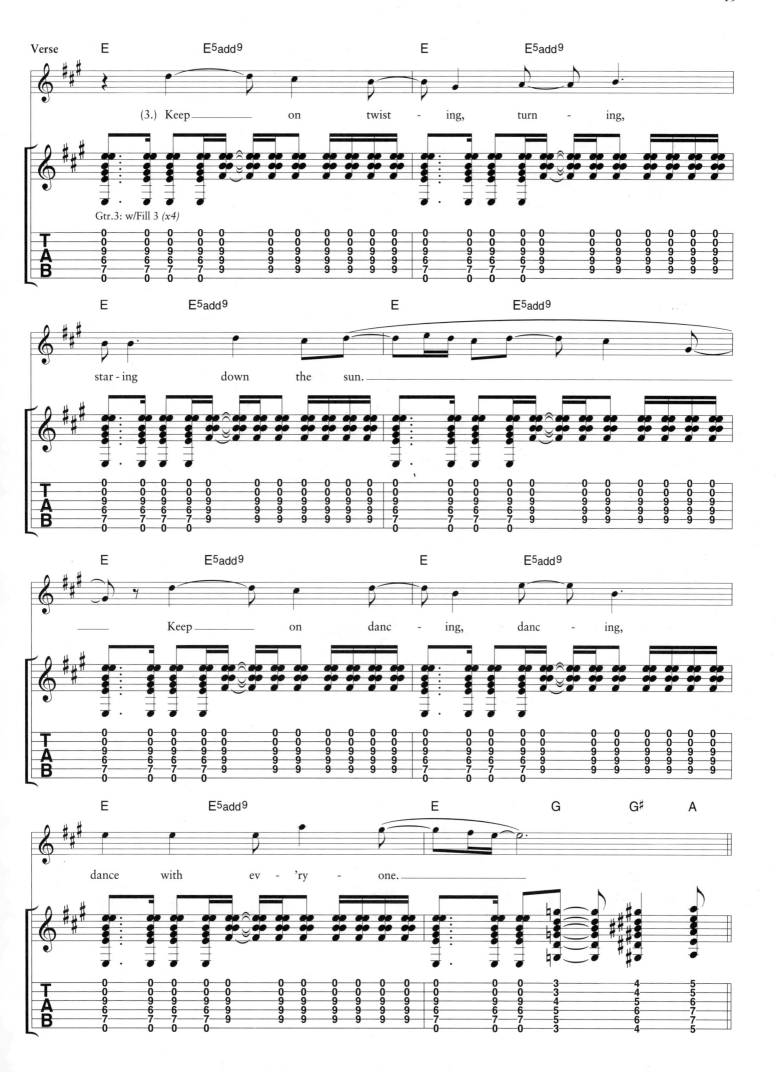

Bring It On

**Words and Music by
Ian Thomas Ball, Paul Blackburn,
Thomas William Gray, Benjamin Joseph Ottewell
and Oliver James Peacock**

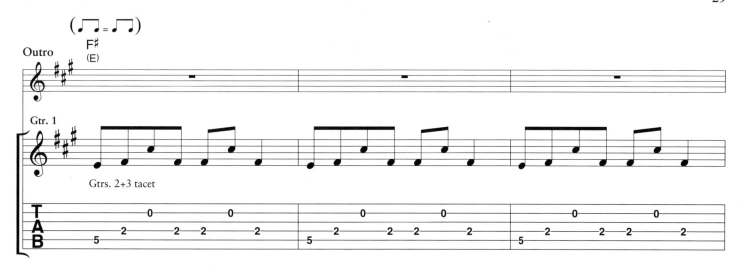

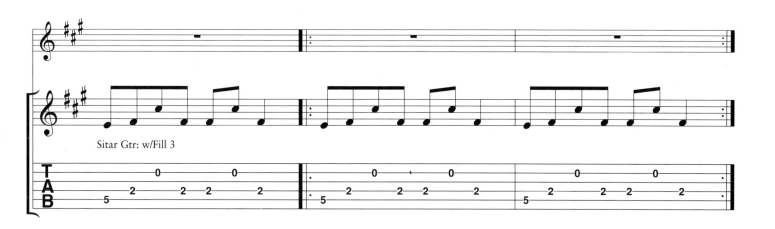

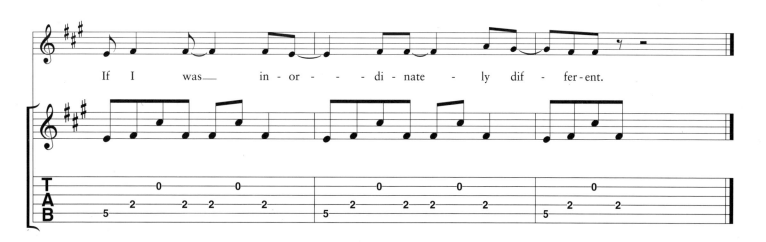

If I was in-or - di - nate - ly dif - fer-ent.

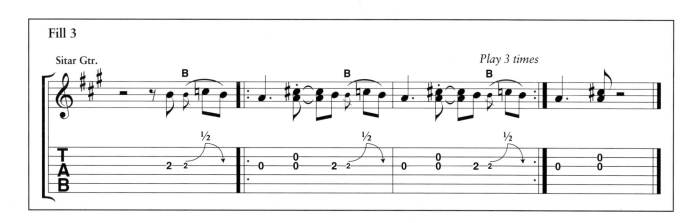

Blue Moon Rising

Words and Music by
Ian Thomas Ball, Paul Blackburn,
Thomas William Gray, Benjamin Joseph Ottewell
and Oliver James Peacock

Gtr. 1: Capo on 4th fret
Gtr. 2: Tune 6th str. down a semitone
Gtr. 3: Standard tuning

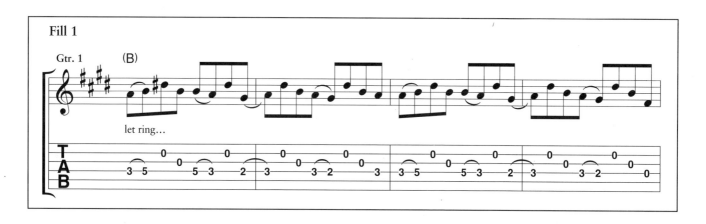

one and all.＿＿＿ Some peo-ple like

that.

(2.) Gon-na

Fill 2

let ring…

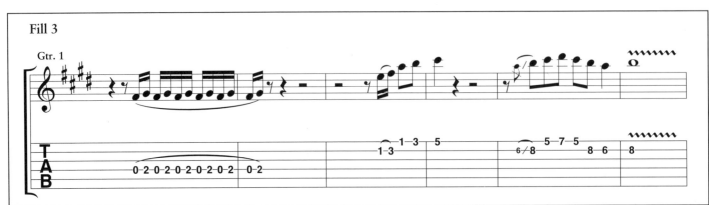

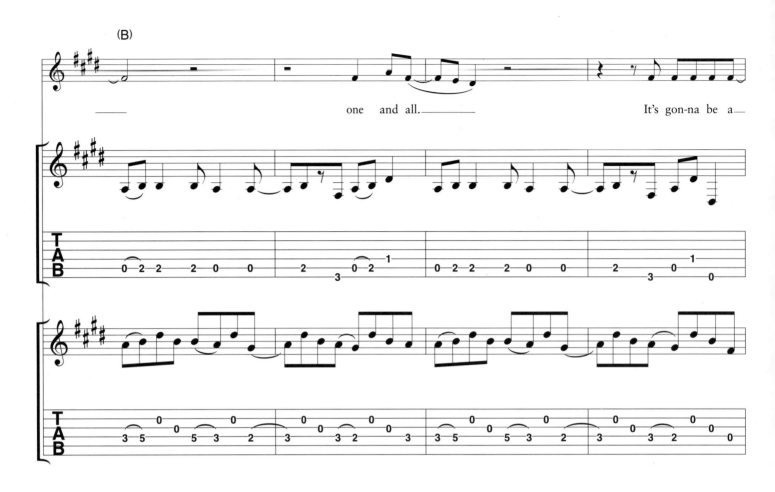

one and all.———

It's gon-na be a—

blue—— moon ris - ing,— ris - - - ing, one and all.—

Las Vegas Dealer

Words and Music by Thomas William Gray,
Oliver James Peacock, Ian Thomas Ball,
Paul Blackburn and Benjamin Joseph Ottewell

40

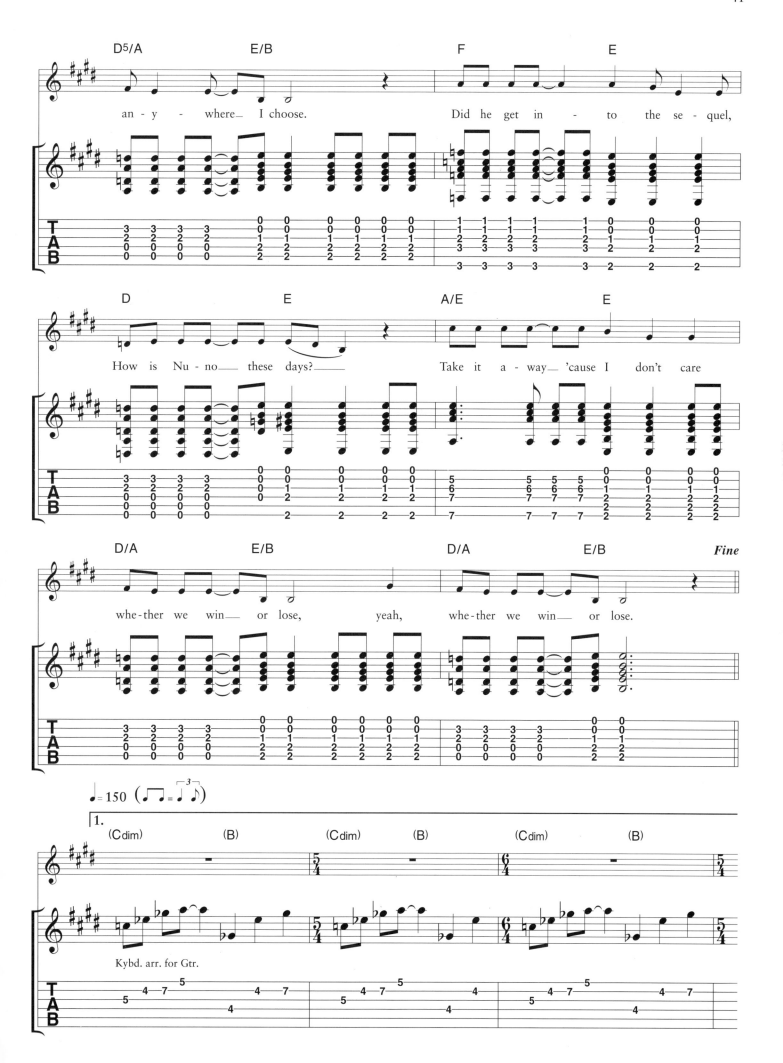

Lyrics:
an-y-where_ I choose.   Did he get in-to the se-quel,

How is Nu-no_ these days?_   Take it a-way_ 'cause I don't care

whe-ther we win_ or lose,   yeah,   whe-ther we win_ or lose.

Kybd. arr. for Gtr.

We Haven't Turned Around

Words and Music by
Thomas William Gray, Oliver James Peacock,
Ian Thomas Ball and Benjamin Joseph Ottewell

Fill My Cup

Words and Music by
Thomas William Gray, Oliver James Peacock,
Ian Thomas Ball, Paul Blackburn
and Benjamin Joseph Ottewell

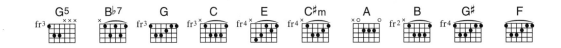

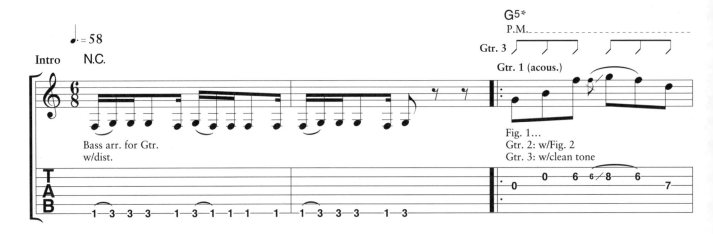

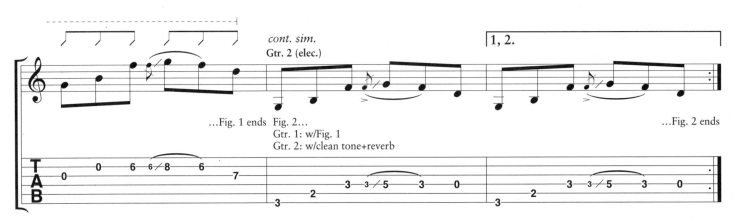

Rhythm and Blues Alibi

Words and Music by
Thomas William Gray, Oliver James Peacock,
Ian Thomas Ball, Benjamin Joseph Ottewell and Paul Blackburn

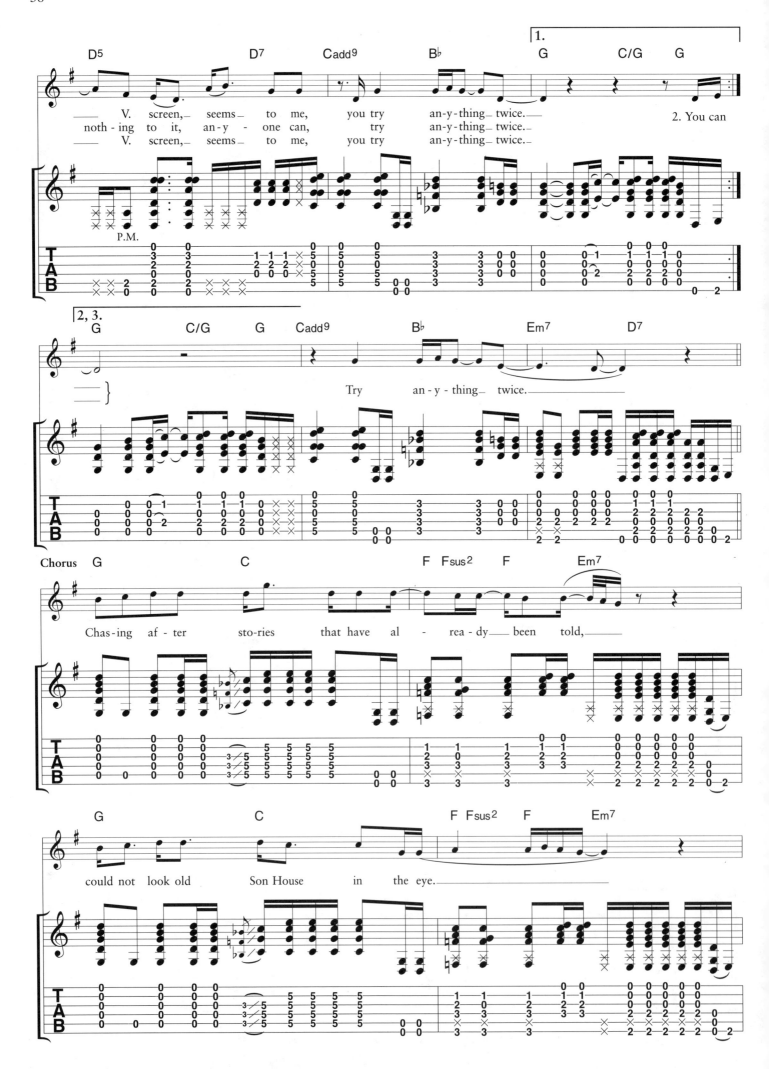

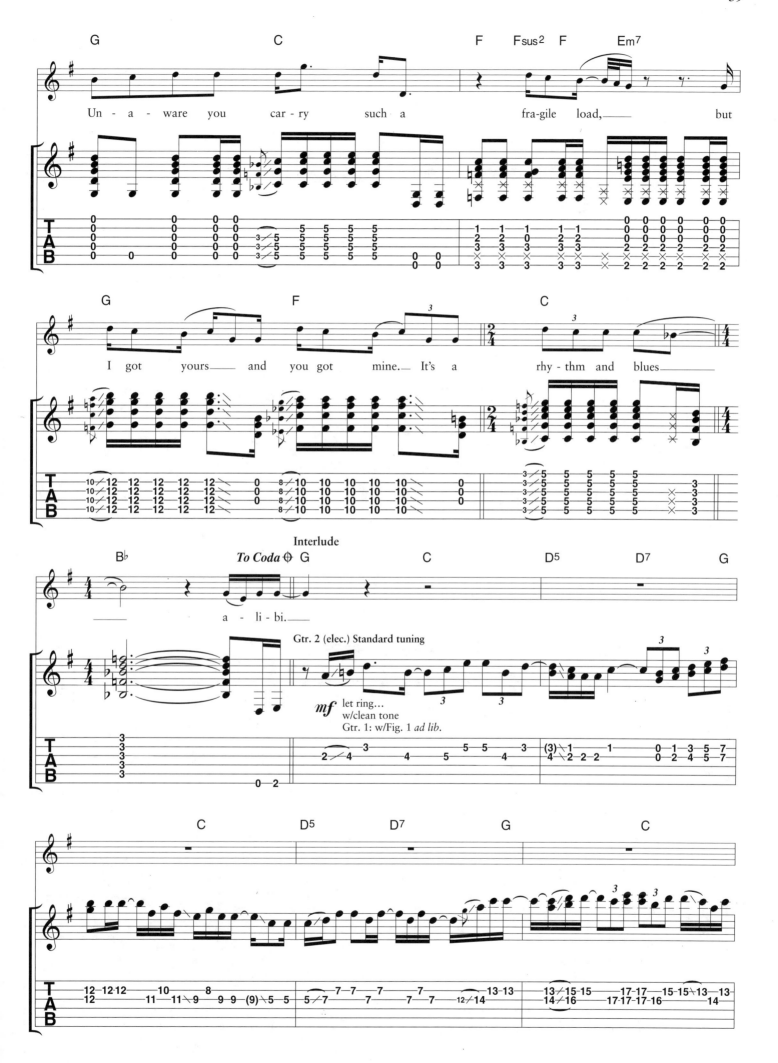

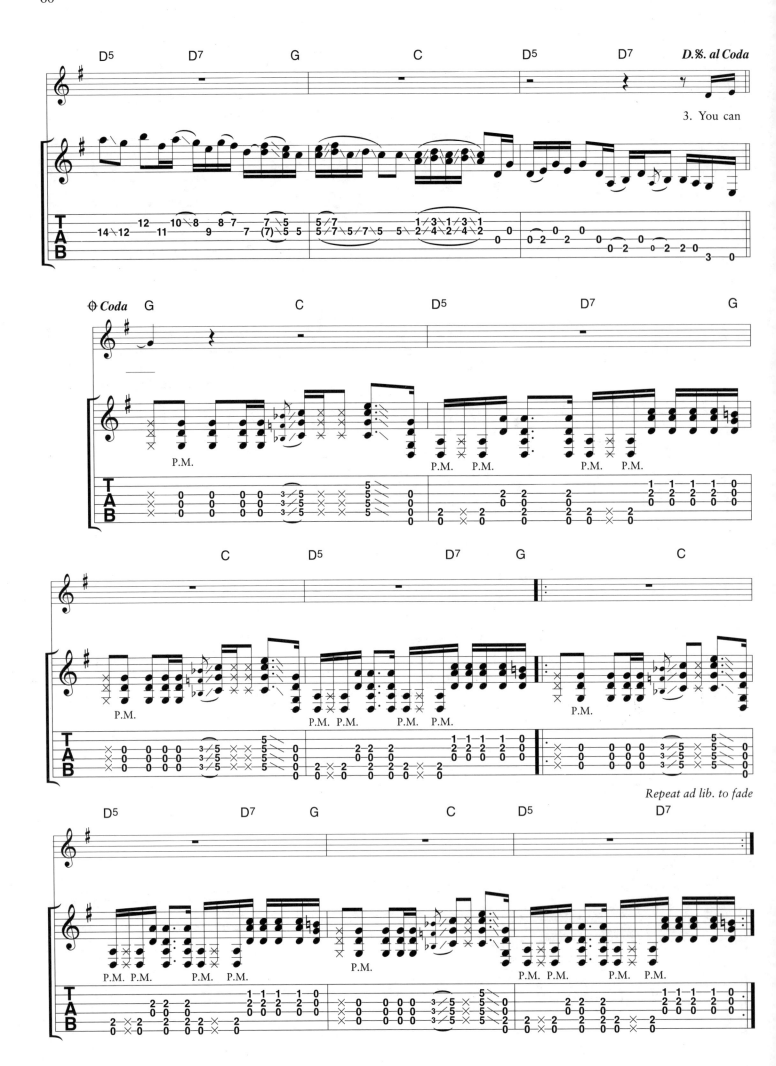

Rosalita

Words and Music by
Thomas William Gray, Oliver James Peacock,
Ian Thomas Ball, Paul Blackburn
and Benjamin Joseph Ottewell

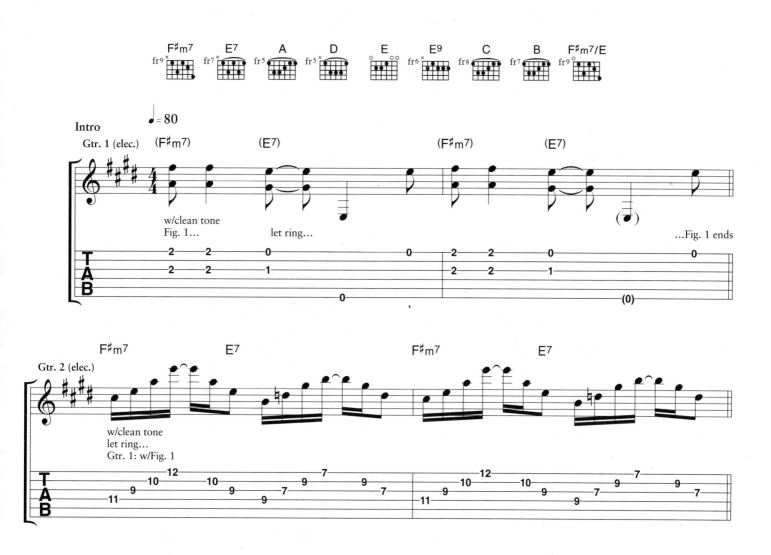

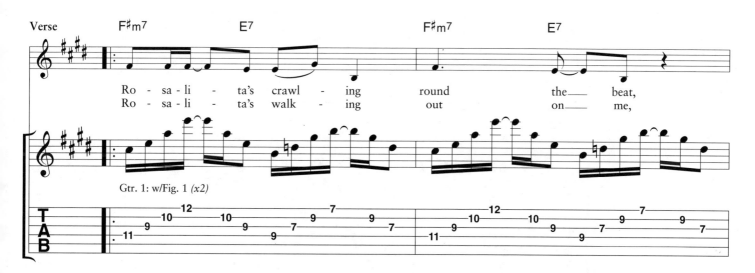

talk to me,— I won't be-tray— my-self— so pi-ti-ful-ly.— My lit-tle con-ceit
study these tears,— your bit-ter words— they just con-firm my fears.— Gon-na let it

—— you see is that I—— will not need you more— than now.
f*** up all the years. Yet I—— will not need you more— than now.

Gtr. 2
Gtr. 1: cont. in slashes

1.
F#m7/E   E7   F#m7   E7

Gtr. 1: w/Fig. 1

2.
Instrumental   E   E9

Gtr. 2: w/finger style
Gtr. 1: w/Fig. 2 *(x2)*

(3.) Beau - ti - ful bitch_____ I could con - si - der this_ a sim - ple_

California

Words and Music by
Thomas William Gray, Oliver James Peacock,
Ian Thomas Ball, Paul Blackburn
and Benjamin Joseph Ottewell

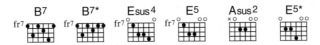

Tune all Guitars down a semitone

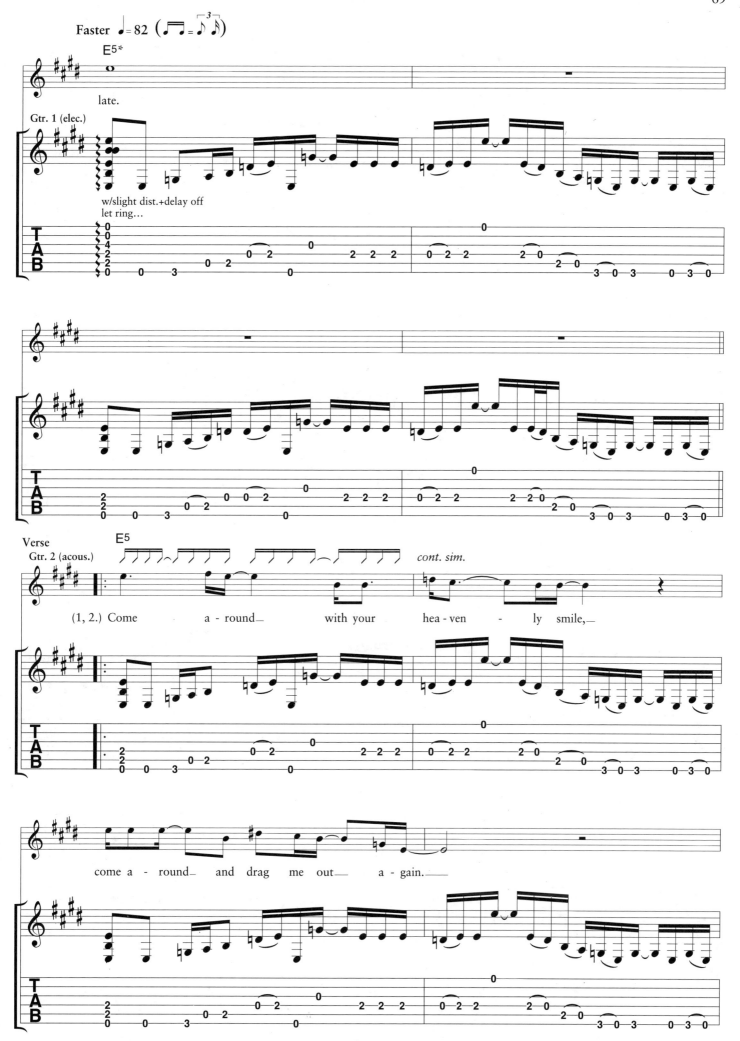

Af - ter——— a while— we can sit and watch— them all—— rush by.—

Come a - round— and drag me out a - gain,——

come a - round and drag me out a - gain.——

Asus 2

Al - ways want - ed to— be, al - ways felt— that I'd— get

Gtrs. 1+2

Gtr. 1: cont. in slashes

2.

Asus2

I could nev - er__ see__ my - self,__ no

I could nev - er__ see__ my - self__ with an - y - bo - dy else.

N.C.

Bass arr. for Gtr.
Gtrs. 1+2: tacet

(1.) If you want a piece of my ass,__ get in line,__
(2.) If you want a kiss, do it fat,__ get in line,__
(3.) If you wan - na prin - cess with a past, get in line,__

Gtr. 1: w/ad lib. fills

(1.) If you want a piece of my ass,___ get in line,___
(2.) If you wan-na kiss, do it fast,___ get in line,___

___ ba - - by get in line.___
___ ba - - by get in line.___

If you want a prin-cess with a past,___ get in line,___
I'll be smil-ing, charm-ing to the last,___ get in line,___

Devil Will Ride

Words and Music by
Thomas William Gray, Oliver James Peacock,
Ian Thomas Ball, Paul Blackburn
and Benjamin Joseph Ottewell

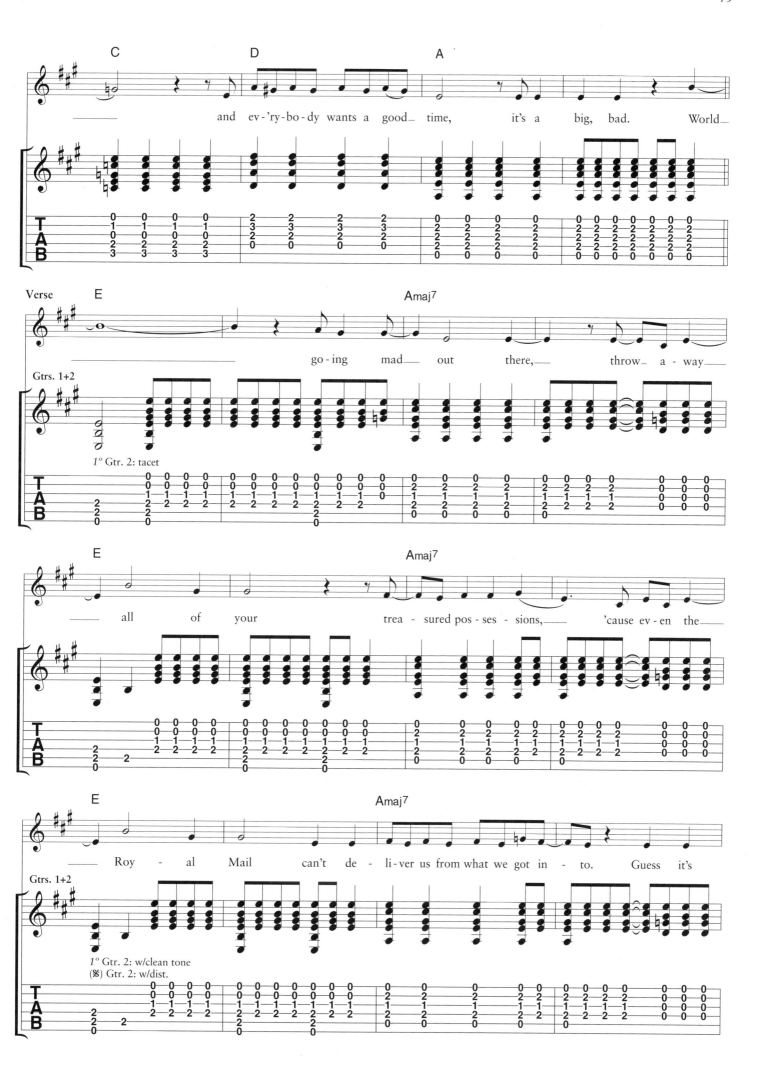

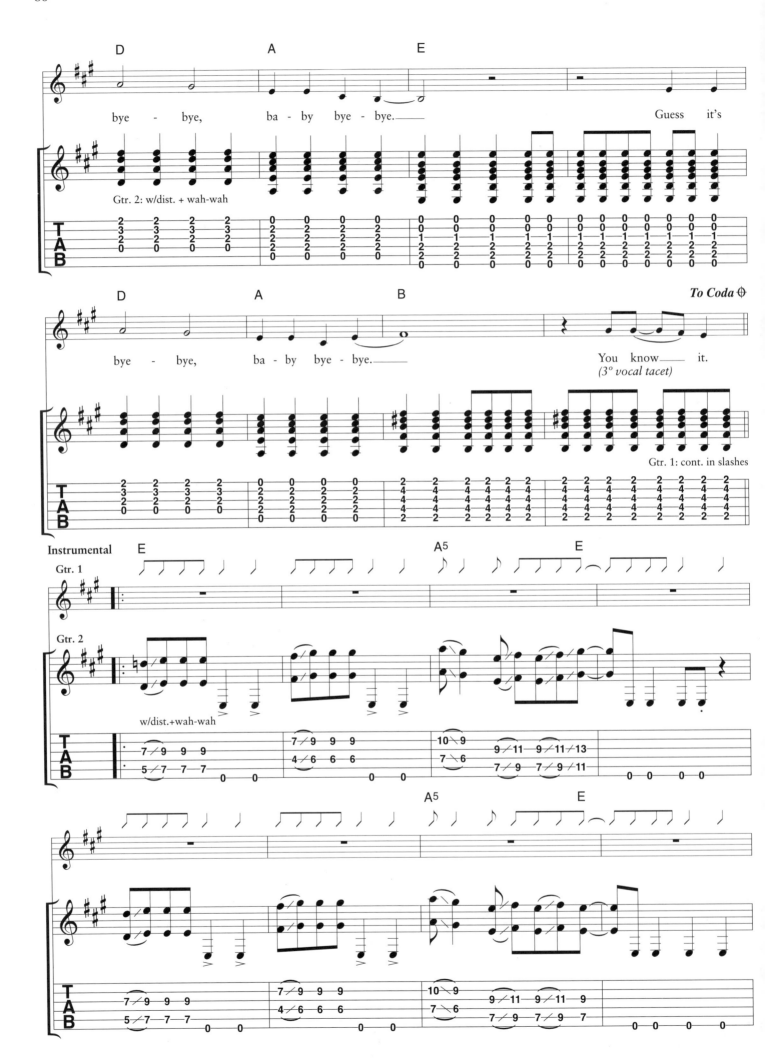

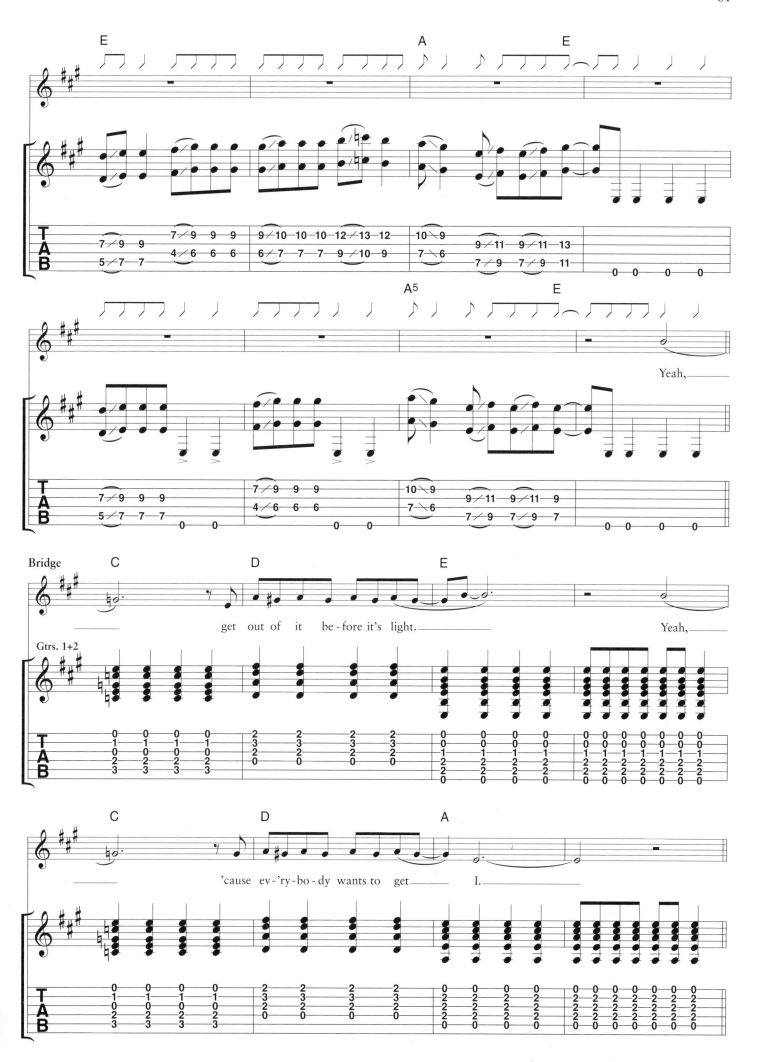

Printed in England
The Panda Group · Haverhill · Suffolk · 4/00

Notation and Tablature Explained

Open C chord

Scale of E major

High E (1st) string
B (2nd) string
G (3rd) string
D (4th) string
A (5th) string
Low E (6th) string

Bent Notes

The note fretted is always shown first. Variations in pitch achieved by string bending are enclosed within this symbol ⌐ ¬. If you aren't sure how far to bend the string, playing the notes indicated without bending gives a guide to the pitches to aim for. The following examples cover the most common string bending techniques:

Example 1
Play the D, bend up one tone (two half-steps) to E.

Example 4
Pre-bend: fret the D, bend up one tone to E, then pick.

Example 2
Play the D, bend up one tone to E then release bend to sound D. Only the first note is picked.

Example 5
Play the A and D together, then bend the B-string up one tone to sound B.

Example 3
Fast bend: Play the D, then bend up one tone to E as quickly as possible.

Example 6
Play the D and F♯ together, then bend the G-string up one tone to E, and the B-string up a semitone to G.

Additional guitaristic techniques have been notated as follows:

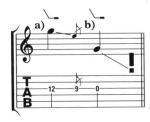

Tremolo Bar
Alter pitch using tremolo bar. Where possible, the pitch to aim for is shown.
a) Play the G; use the bar to drop the pitch to E.
b) Play the open G; use the bar to 'divebomb', i.e. drop the pitch as far as possible.

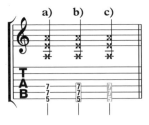

Mutes
a) Right hand mute
Mute strings by resting the right hand on the strings just above the bridge.
b) Left hand mute
Damp the strings by releasing left hand pressure just after the notes sound.
c) Unpitched mute
Damp the strings with the left hand to produce a percussive sound.

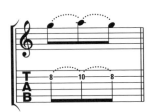

Hammer on and Pull off
Play first note, sound next note by 'hammering on', the next by 'pulling off'. Only the first note is picked.

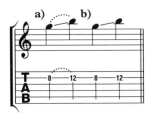

Glissando
a) Play first note, sound next note by sliding up string. Only the first note is picked.
b) As above, but pick second note.

Natural Harmonics
Touch the string over the fret marked, and pick to produce a bell-like tone. The small notes show the resultant pitch, where necessary.

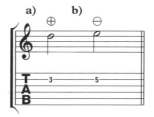

Slide Guitar
a) Play using slide.
b) Play without slide.

Artificial Harmonics
Fret the lowest note, touch string over fret indicated by diamond notehead and pick. Small notes show the resultant pitch.

Vibrato
Apply vibrato, by 'shaking' note or with tremolo bar. As vibrato is so much a matter of personal taste and technique, it is indicated only where essential.

Pinch Harmonics
Fret the note as usual, but 'pinch' or 'squeeze' the string with the picking hand to produce a harmonic overtone. Small notes show the resultant pitch.

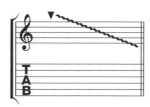

Pick Scratch
Scrape the pick down the strings – this works best on the wound strings.

Microtones
A downwards arrow means the written pitch is lowered by less than a semitone; an upwards arrow raises the written pitch.

Repeated Chords
To make rhythm guitar parts easier to read the tablature numbers may be omitted when a chord is repeated. The example shows a C major chord played naturally, r/h muted, l/h muted and as an unpitched mute respectively.

Special Tunings
Non-standard tunings are shown as 'tuning boxes'. Each box represents one guitar string, the leftmost box corresponding to the lowest pitched string. The symbol '•' in a box means the pitch of the corresponding string is not altered. A note within a box means the string must be re-tuned as stated. For tablature readers, numbers appear in the boxes. The numbers represent the number of half-steps the string must be tuned up or down. The tablature relates to an instrument tuned as stated.

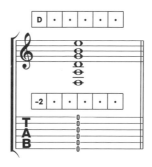

Tune the low E (6th) string down one tone (two half-steps) to D.

Chord naming
The following chord naming convention has been used:

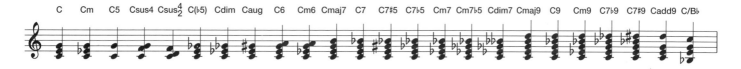

Where there is no appropriate chord box, for example when the music consists of a repeated figure (or riff) the tonal base is indicated in parenthesis: [C]

Where it was not possible to transcribe a passage, the symbol ∼ appears.

Indications sur la notation musicale et les tablatures

Accord de Do majeur ouvert

Gamme de Mi majeur

Mi aigu: 1ère corde
Si: 2e corde
Sol: 3e corde
Ré: 4e corde
La: 5e corde
Mi grave: 6e corde

Bending

La note correspondant à la case sur laquelle on pose le doigt est toujours indiquée en premier. Les variations de hauteur sont obtenues en poussant sur la corde et sont indiquées par le symbole: ⌐‾⌐. En cas de doute sur la hauteur à atteindre, le fait de jouer les notes indiquées sans pousser sur la corde permet de trouver ensuite la bonne hauteur. Les examples suivants démontrent les techniques de bending les plus courantes.

Exemple 1
Jouez la note Ré et poussez la corde d'un ton (deux demi-tons) pour atteindre le Mi.

Exemple 4
'Pre-bend': posez le doigt sur la case de Ré, poussez d'un ton pour atteindre le Mi avant de jouer la note.

Exemple 2
Jouez le Ré, poussez sur la corde pour atteindre le Mi un ton plus haut, relâchez ensuite pour revenir au Ré. Seule la première note est jouée avec le médiator.

Exemple 5
Jouez La et Ré simultanément; poussez ensuite sur la corde de Si pour atteindre la note Si.

Exemple 3
'Fast Bend': jouez le Ré et poussez le plus rapidement possible pour atteindre le Mi.

Exemple 6
Jouez Ré et Fa♯ simultanément; poussez la corde de Sol d'un ton vers le Mi, et la corde de Si d'un demi-ton vers le Sol.

D'autres techniques de guitare sont notées de la façon suivante:

Emploi du levier de vibrato
Modifiez la hauteur du son avec le levier de vibrato. Lorsque c'est possible, la note à atteindre est indiquée.
a) Jouez le Sol et appuyez sur le levier de vibrato pour atteindre le Mi.
b) Jouez un Sol à vide et détendez le plus possible la corde avec le levier de vibrato pour rendre un effect de 'bombe qui tombe' (divebomb).

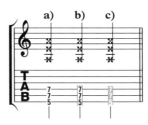

Mutes (étouffements)
a) Mute de la main droite
Etouffez en posant la main droite sur les cordes, au-dessus du chevalet.
b) Mute de la main gauche
Relâchez la pression sur la corde juste après avoir joué la note.
c) Mute sans hauteur définie
Etouffez les cordes avec la main gauche pour obtenir un son de percussion.

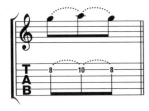

Hammer On et Pull Off
Jouez la première note; frappez la corde sur la touche (Hammer On) pour obtenir la seconde note, et relâchez la seconde note en tirant sur la corde (Pull Off) pour obtenir la troisième note. Seule la première note est done jouée avec le médiator.

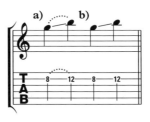

Glissando
a) Jouez la première note avec le médiator, faites sonner la seconde note en ne faisant que glisser le doigt sur la corde.
b) Comme ci-dessus, mais en attaquant également la seconde note avec le médiator.

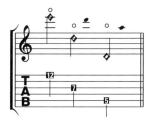

Harmoniques naturelles

Posez le doigt sur la corde au dessus de la barrette indiquée, et jouez avec le médiator pour obtenir un son cristallin. Le cas échéant, une petite note indique la hauteur du son que l'on doit obtenir.

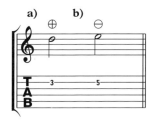

Guitare Slide

a) Note jouée avec le slide.
b) Note jouée sans le slide.

Harmoniques artificielles

Posez le doigt (main gauche) sur la note la plus basse: effleurez la corde avec l'index de la main droite au-dessus de la barrette indiquée par la note en forme de losange, tout en actionnant le médiator. La petite note indique la hauteur du son que l'on doit obtenir.

Effet de Vibrato

Jouez le vibrato soit avec le doigt sur la corde (main gauche), soit avec le levier de vibrato. Comme le vibrato est une affaire de technique et de goût personnels, il n'est indiqué que quand cela est vraiment nécessaire.

Harmoniques pincées

Appuyez le doigt sur la corde de la façon habituelle, mais utilisez conjointement le médiator et l'index de la main droite de façon à obtenir une harmonique aiguë. Les petites notes indiquent la hauteur du son que l'on doit obtenir.

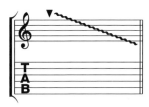

Scratch

Faites glisser le médiator du haut en bas de la corde. Le meilleur effet est obtenu avec des cordes filetées.

Quarts de ton

Une flèche dirigée vers le bas indique que la note est baissée d'un quart-de-ton. Une flèche dirigée vers le haut indique que la note est haussée d'un quart-de-ton.

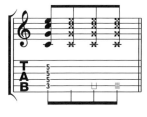

Accords répétés

Pour faciliter la lecture des parties de guitare rythmique, les chiffres de tablature sont omis quand l'accord est répété. L'example montre successivement un accord de Do majeur joué de façon normale, un 'mute' de la main droite, un 'mute' de la main gauche et un 'mute' sans hauteur définie.

Accordages spéciaux

Les accordages non-standards sont indiqués par six cases, chacune représentant une corde (de gauche à droite), de la plus grave à la plus aiguê. Un tiret indique que la tension de la corde correspondante ne doit pas être altérée. Un nom de note indique la nouvelle note à obtenir. Pour les tablatures, les chiffres indiqués dans les cases représentent le nombre de demi-tons dont ou doit désaccorder la corde, vers le haut ou vers le bas.

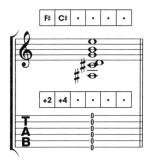

Accordez la corde de Mi grave un ton plus haut de façon à obtenir un Fa#, et la corde de La deux tons plus haut de façon à obtenir un Do#.

Noms des accords

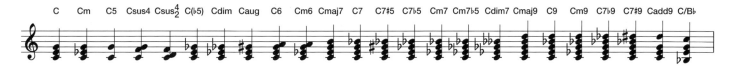

Lorsqu'aucun nom d'accord précis n'est applicable, par exemple quand la musique consiste en une figure répétée (riff), le centre tonal est indiqué entre parenthèses: [C]

Lorsqu'un passage n'a pas pu être transcrit, le symbole ∿ apparait.

Hinweise zu Notation und Tabulatur

Offener C - Dur - Akkord

E - Dur - Tonleiter

Hohe E-Saite (1.)
H-Saite (2.)
G-Saite (3.)
D-Saite (4.)
A-Saite (5.)
Tiefe E-Saite (6.)

Gezogene Noten

Die gegriffene Note wird immer zuerst angegeben. Das Zeichen ⌐ ¬ zeigt eine Veränderung der Tonhöhe an, die durch das Ziehen der Saiten erreicht wird. Falls Du nicht sicher bist, wie weit die Saite gezogen werden soll, spiele die entsprechenden Töne zunächst ohne Ziehen; so kannst Du Dich an der Tonhöhe orientieren. Die folgenden Beispiele geben die gebräuchlichsten Techniken zum Ziehen wieder:

Beispiel 1
Spiele das D und ziehe dann um einen Ton (zwei Halbtonschritte) höher zum E.

Beispiel 4
Im Voraus gezogen: Greife das D, ziehe um einen Ton höher zum E und schlage erst dann die Saite an.

Beispiel 2
Spiele das D, ziehe um einen Ton hoch zum E und dann wieder zurück, so daß D erklingt. Dabei wird nur die erste Note angeschlagen.

Beispiel 5
Spiele A und D gleichzeitig und ziehe dann die H-Saite um einen Ton nach oben, so daß H erklingt.

Beispiel 3
Schnelles Ziehen: Spiele das D und ziehe dann so schnell Du kannst um einen Ton höher zum E.

Beispiel 6
Spiele D und Fis gleichzeitig; ziehe dann die G-Saite um einen Ton nach oben zum E und die H-Saite um einen Halbtonschritt nach oben zum G.

Zusätzliche Spieltechniken für Gitarre wurden folgendermaßen notiert:

Tremolo
Verändere die Tonhöhe mit dem Tremolo-Hebel. Wenn es möglich ist, wird die angestrebte Tonhöhe angezeigt.
a) Spiele G; nutze den Takt, um zum E abzusteigen.
b) Spiele die leere G-Saite; nutze den Takt, um so weit wie möglich abzusteigen.

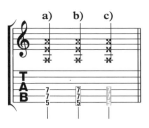

Dämpfen
a) Mit der rechten Hand
Dämpfe die Saiten, indem Du die rechte Hand einfach oberhalb der Brücke auf die Saiten legst.
b) Mit der linken Hand
Dämpfe die Saiten, indem Du den Druck der linken Hand löst, kurz nachdem die Töne erklingen.
c) Ohne bestimmte Tonhöhe
Dämpfe die Saiten mit der linken Hand; so erzielst Du einen 'geschlagenen' Sound.

Hammer on und Pull off
Spiele die erste Note; die zweite erklingt durch 'Hammering on', die dritte durch 'Pulling off'. Dabei wird nur die erste Note angeschlagen.

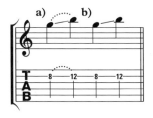

Glissando
a) Spiele die erste Note; die zweite erklingt durch Hochrutschen des Fingers auf der Saite. Nur die erste Note wird angeschlagen.
b) Wie oben, aber die zweite Note wird angeschlagen.

Natürliches Flageolett
Berühre die Saite über dem angegebenen Bund; wenn Du jetzt anschlägst, entsteht ein glockenähnlicher Ton. Wo es nötig ist, zeigen kleine Notenköpfe die entstandene Note an.

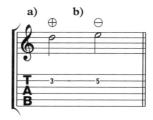

Slide Guitar
a) Spiele mit Rutschen des Fingers.
b) Spiele ohne Rutschen.

Künstliches Flageolett
Greife die unterste Note, berühre die Saite über dem durch Rauten angegebenen Bund und schlage dann den Ton an. Die kleinen Notenköpfe zeigen wieder die entstandene Note an.

Vibrato
Beim Vibrato läßt Du die Note für die Dauer eines Tons durch Druckvariation oder Tremolo-Hebel 'beben'. Da es jedoch eine Frage des persönlichen Geschmacks ist, wird Vibrato nur dort angegeben, wo es unerläßlich ist.

Gezupftes Flageolett
Greife die Note ganz normal, aber drücke die Saite mit der zupfenden Hand so, daß ein harmonischer Oberton entsteht. Kleine Notenköpfe zeigen den entstandenen Ton an.

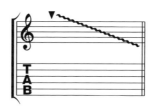

Pick Scratch
Fahre mit dem Plektrum nach unten über die Saiten – das klappt am besten bei umsponnenen Saiten.

Vierteltöne
Ein nach unten gerichteter Pfeil bedeutet, daß die notierte Tonhöhe um einen Viertelton erniedrigt wird; ein nach oben gerichteter Pfeil bedeutet, daß die notierte Tonhöhe um einen Viertelton erhöht wird.

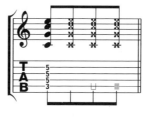

Akkordwiederholung
Um die Stimmen für Rhythmus-Gitarre leichter lesbar zu machen, werden die Tabulaturziffern weggelassen, wenn ein Akkord wiederholt werden soll. Unser Beispiel zeigt einen C - Dur - Akkord normal gespielt, rechts gedämpft, links gedämpft und ohne Tonhöhe.

Besondere Stimmung
Falls eine Stimmung verlangt wird, die vom Standard abweicht, wird sie in Kästchen angegeben. Jedes Kästchen steht für eine Saite, das erste links außen entspricht der tiefsten Saite. Wenn die Tonhöhe einer Saite nicht verändert werden soll, enthält das Kästchen einen Punkt. Steht eine Note im Kästchen, muß die Saite wie angegeben umgestimmt werden. In der Tabulaturschrift stehen stattdessen Ziffern im entsprechenden Kästchen: Sie geben die Zahl der Halbtonschritte an, um die eine Saite höher oder tiefer gestimmt werden soll.

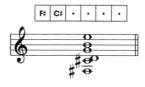

Stimme die tiefe E-Saite (6.) um einen Ganzton (zwei Halbtonschritte) höher auf Fis und die A-Saite (5.) um zwei Ganztöne (vier Halbtonschritte) höher auf Cis.

Akkordbezeichnung
Die folgenden Akkordbezeichnungen wurden verwendet.

Wenn kein eigenes Akkordsymbol angegeben ist, z.B. bei Wiederholung einer musikalischen Figur (bzw. Riff), steht die Harmoniebezeichnung in Klammern: [C]

Das Symbol ∿ steht jeweils dort, wo es nicht möglich war, einen Abschnitt zu übertragen.

Spiegazione della notazione e dell'intavolatura

Accordo di Do aperto
(in prima posizione)

Scala di Mi maggiore

Mi acuto: la corda
Si: 2a corda
Sol: 3a corda
Re: 4a corda
La: 5a corda
Mi basso: 6a corda

Bending

La prima nota scritta è sempre quella tastata normalmente. Le alterazioni di altezza da realizzare con la trazione laterale della corda (bending) interessano le note comprese sotto al segno: ⌐ ‾ ⌐. Se siete incerti sull'entità dell'innalzamento di tono da raggiungere, suonate le note indicate tastando normalmente la corda. Gli esempi seguenti mostrano le tecniche più comunemente impiegate nella maggior parte dei casi che possono presentarsi.

Esempio 1
Suonate il Re e innalzate di un tono (due mezzi toni) a Mi.

Esempio 4
'Pre-Bend': tastate il Re, tirate alzando di un tono a Mi e poi suonate.

Esempio 2
Suonate il Re, tirate alzando di un tono a Mi e rilasciate tornando a Re. Va suonata solo la prima nota.

Esempio 5
Suonate simultaneamente La e Si quindi tirate la 2a corda per innalzare il suono a Si.

Esempio 3
'Bend Veloce': suonate il Re e quindi alzate di un tono a Mi il più velocemente possibile.

Esempio 6
Suonate simultaneamente Re e Fa# quindi tirate la 3a corda alzando il suono di un tono a Mi, e la 2a corda di mezzo tono, alzando il suono a Sol.

Negli esempi seguenti sono illustrate altre tecniche chitarristiche:

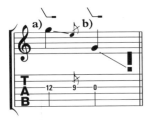

Barra del tremolo
Alterate l'altezza del suono mediante la barra del tremolo. Dove possibile l'altezza da raggiungere è indicata.
a) Suonate il Sol e abbassate il suono fino a Mi mediante la barra.
b) Suonate il Sol a vuoto e scendete quanto più possibile.

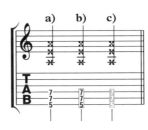

Smorzato
a) Smorzato con la destra
Smorzare le corde con il palmo della mano destra in prossimità del ponticello.
b) Smorzato con la sinistra
Smorzare le corde allentando la pressione delle dita subito dopo aver prodotto i suoni.
c) Pizzicato
Premere leggermente le corde in modo che non producano note ma soltanto un effetto percussivo.

Legature ascendenti e discendenti
Suonate la prima nota e ricavate la seconda percuotendo la corda con il dito contro la barretta; per la terza nota tirate la corda con il medesimo dito. Soltano la prima nota va suonata.

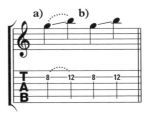

Glissando
a) Suonate la prima nota e ricavare la seconda facendo scivolare il dito lungo la corda. Va pizzicata solo la prima nota.
b) Come sopra, ma pizzicando anche la seconda nota.

Armonici naturali
Toccate leggermente la corda sulla barretta indicata e pizzicate col plettro per produrre un suono di campana. Le notine indicano il suono risultante, dove occorra.

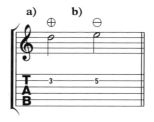

Slide Chitarra
a) Suonare con slide.
b) Suonare senza slide.

Armonici artificiali
Tastate la nota più bassa, toccate leggermente la corda sulla barretta relativa alla nota romboidale e pizzicate con il plettro. Le notine indicano il suono risultante.

Vibrato
Effettuate il vibrato facendo oscillare il dito che preme la corda oppure con la barra del tremolo. Poichè il vibrato è un fatto di gusto personale, viene indicato solo dove è essenziale.

Armonici pizzicati
Tastate normalmente la nota ma pizzicate la corda con la mano destra per ricavare l'armonico sopracuto. Le notine indicano l'altezza del suono risultante.

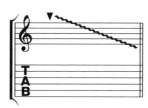

Suono graffiato
Fate scorrere il bordo del plettro lungo la corda. L'effetto è maggiore sulle corde fasciate.

Microintervalli
Una freccia diretta verso il basso significa che il suono scritto va abbassato di un intervallo inferiore al semitono; una freccia diretta verso l'alto innalza il suono scritto.

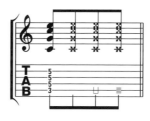

Accordi ripetuti
Per facilitare la lettura, possono venire omessi i numeri nell'intavolatura di un accordo ripetuto. L'esempio mostra un accordi di Do maggiore suonato normalmente, smorzato con la destra, smorzato con la sinistra e pizzicato (muto).

Accordature Speciali
Le accordature diverse da quella normale sono indicate in speciali 'gabbie di accordatura'. Ogni gabbia rappresenta una corda di chitarra; all'estremità sinistra corrisponde la corda più bassa. Il simbolo '·' in una gabbia sta ad indicare che l'intonazione della corda corrispondente è quella normale. Una nota nella gabbia indica che l'intonazione di quella corda va modificata portandola all'altezza indicata. Per coloro che leggono l'intavolatura, dei numeri posti nelle gabbie stanno ad indicare di quanti semitoni deve salire o scendere l'intonazione della corda. L'intavolatura è da considerarsi relativa ad uno strumento accordato come indicato nelle gabbie.

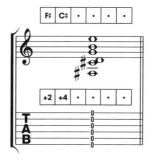

Accordate la corda del Mi basso (6a) un tono sopra (due semitoni) a Fa#. Accordate la corda del La basso (5a) due toni sopra (quattro semitoni) a Do#.

Indicazione degli accordi
E' stata impiegata la seguente nomenclatura convenzionale degli accordi.

Quando non compare la griglia appropriata di un accordo, ad esempio, quando la musica consiste nella ripetizione di una stessa figura (riff), la base tonale è indicata fra parentesi: **[C]**

Dove non è stato possibile trascivere il passaggio, compare il segno ∼ .

Printed in England
The Panda Group · Haverhill · Suffolk · 4/00